CurricuLinks

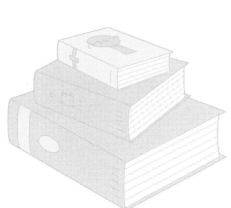

Creative Publications

Author: Kim Saxe
Editor: Ann Roper
Designer: Janice Kawamoto
Production Coordinator: Ed Lazar
Production Services: Morgan-Cain & Assoc.

The activities in this book were taken from *Making Connections* in MathLand™, a K–6 mathematics series by Creative Publications.

© 1995 Creative Publications
1300 Villa Street
Mountain View, California 94041
Printed in U.S.A.

ISBN: 1-56107-777-1
1 2 3 4 5 6 7 8 9 10   99 98 97 96 95

Table of Contents

GEOMETRY AND VISUAL THINKING

LOGIC AND ALGEBRA

MEASUREMENT

PROBABILITY AND STATISTICS

Notes to the Teacher

WHAT IS CURRICULINKS?

CurricuLinks links the mathematical strands recommended by the National Council of Teachers of Mathematics with other areas of the curriculum. There are three books in the series, for grades K - 2, 3 - 4, and 5 - 6. Each of them is rich with ideas for activities to link math to the other subject areas you cover each year. For example, a study of measurement might be carried over to a social studies lesson on the relative size (area) of different islands. Or a math lesson on fractions could be supplemented by a cooking experience.

WHAT ARE THE NCTM STRANDS?

The National Council of Teachers of Mathematics has identified several important mathematical strands upon which many current math programs are based. The strands identified for the CurricuLinks series are:

- Number Relations
- Measurement
- Geometry and Visual Thinking
- Logic and Algebra
- Data Analysis
- Patterns and Relationships
- Probability and Statistics

The strands overlap each other. The study of measurement involves number relations and perhaps visual thinking. Patterns and relationships are found throughout number relations and logic. With CurricuLinks you can weave the strands through other areas of your curriculum, to make schoolwork meaningful and exciting for your students.

WHAT ARE THE CONNECTIONS?

The activities are grouped under the seven strands. In this book there are 13 different areas to which these strands connect. These areas are listed below; those in bold have the most connections to them.

Art	**Multicultural Activities**	Cooking
Music	Dramatic Play	Physical Education
Literature	Reference Skills	Games/Creativity
Science	Language Arts	Social Studies
Technology		

HOW DO I USE THIS BOOK?

You can use this book in two ways. You can extend a math lesson by looking for an interesting connection with which to enrich it. Or, you can broaden a unit in another curriculum area by looking for a math topic with which to correlate it. As an example, if your math focus is geometry, you might try a literature connection, reading and showing a book of photographs to the class about shapes in our everyday world. Alternatively, if you are looking for some books for the library corner, you could connect literature with geometry by choosing some books about shapes, both recognizing and making them.

Each of these activities is equivalent to one lesson or a mini-lesson. You can present it to the class to work on as a whole, in groups, or in pairs of two students. In some activities we recommend one particular way of grouping. Few supplies are required; some activities need a minimum of advance preparation.

Each of the seven sections of the book ends with a Literature List. Here you will find books dealing with topics in that strand. In some cases, a book is included in an activity described in that section. The lists contain mostly books for young people, but a few are for adults or may be enjoyed by both children and adults. Some of the books are reference books that will be helpful in completing some of the activities in that section.

CurricuLinks projects can be ongoing activities, in some cases, or projects to return to at a later time. Sometimes you, as the teacher, may need to change the focus. An activity that suggests having students write reports could be changed to having them give oral presentations or present their facts in a dramatic or artistic way. Be flexible, and fit the material to your students and your way of doing things. We hope you will enjoy using CurricuLinks and find the world of math connections rich and inviting.

Number Relations

BUILDING A NETWORK OF NUMBER RELATIONS

The activities in this section help students develop their skills and confidence in counting, discover the relationships between numbers and express them using an equation format, and work with larger numbers by using groups of tens and ones.

Some of the activities give children an opportunity to refine their skill with counting. Using songs, active games, and literature, children will become more comfortable using numbers in their world.

The students will begin to think about numbers in relation to other numbers and to talk about these relationships in meaningful ways. They will have abundant opportunities to use the language of mathematics to describe what they see and do with objects. Some of the activities encourage children to write equations to record actions taken with objects which aids them in understanding the meaning of addition and subtraction. In general, the movement is from the informal language of the child, to the more formal language of mathematics, to the social convention of recording in an equation format.

What do the experts say?

We now know that chanting addition tables or memorizing number facts is not the way to a real understanding of number relationships. For these to be meaningful and interrelated, children must be allowed to discover the relationships for themselves. The teacher's task is to contrive situations in such a way that . . . children will make these discoveries.

Nuffield Mathematics Project
Mathematics Begins

Hidden Numerals

ART CONNECTION

 Children will have fun playing Mystery Numbers with finger paints while learning kinesthetically how to draw the different numerals. Have each child make a finger painting in which she or he hides several numerals. Pairs of children then try to locate and name all of the hidden numerals in each other's paintings. Once all the numerals have been discovered, the children can smear over their paintings and play the game again. This activity could also be done using pudding in a resealable plastic bag.

Another activity that gives students some practice with numeral writing and recognition is using numerals as parts of objects in a drawing or painting. The number 11 could form the sides of a chimney, for example. The class will enjoy finding the hidden numerals in each other's art work.

How Many Legs? Scavenger Hunt

SCIENCE CONNECTION

Have a How Many Legs? scavenger hunt. Place ten sheets of large paper, labeled at the top with one of the numbers from zero to nine, on table tops. On these papers, have the students draw pictures of animals that have that many legs. Have a stack of nature books or magazines available as a resource.

The children will have some ideas as to whether or not they'll be able to find an animal for any particular number. Much interesting conversation ensues. When completed, assemble the children's work into a class book.

This could also be a great activity during a field trip to the zoo, with children drawing pictures of the animals on sheets of paper. They could then glue the pictures to the appropriate large sheets when they return to school.

Counting Around the World

MULTICULTURAL CONNECTION

 Read aloud *Moja Means One* by Muriel Feelings (Dial, 1971), which introduces counting in the Swahili language. When the children feel comfortable with this counting, have them record their efforts on tape, singly, all together, or in groups.

Ask if anyone knows how to count in a language other than English. If you have immediate responses, tape each child's counting. If several children speak the same language, they can count in chorus. Some children may have family members who could help add to your number recordings. See if these children can learn more counting at home and bring it back to the class.

Number Art: Thirteen 123s from Around the World by Leonard Everett Fisher (Four Winds, 1982) could be used as a resource for words for oral counting in many languages. After taping the students counting in these languages, you could lead them in making a chart of the numbers one to ten in a few different languages.

Save the tapes you make. Perhaps, as the year progresses, you can add some number rhymes and songs in both English and other languages.

Millie's Math House

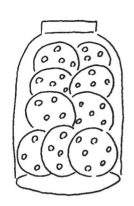

TECHNOLOGY CONNECTION

Millie's Math House, Edmark
Macintosh, MS-DOS

To reinforce counting skills, show children how to select the Number Machine in the center of the screen. Children click on any number from zero to ten and count out loud the critters that pop up.

Children use thinking and counting skills in the Cookie Factory. Show them how to select it by clicking on the cookie jar. To make a cookie appear, click on the cookie pipe. Click the conveyor belt lever to move the cookie under the jelly bean dispenser. Decorate the cookie by clicking the jelly bean dispenser. The number of jelly beans will be counted out loud and shown on the jelly bean meter as they drop onto the cookie. Click on the hand to move the cookie into a cookie bin.

Reinforce the Cookie Factory activity in *Millie's Math House* by having the children make some Yummy Numbers. Set out graham cracker squares spread with cream cheese on which the children can arrange raisins. Choose a number of raisins (six, for example) for the children to put on each cracker, and challenge the children to make different arrangements. Admire all the designs, then eat.

Counting in the Block Corner

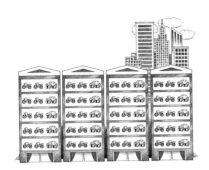

GAMES/CREATIVITY CONNECTION

 Have the children build tall towers or other structures with blocks, and ask them some questions about what they are doing. When a tower falls, they can estimate, count, and record how many blocks were used. Ask how many blocks there were in that tower. Children can compare recordings to see who made a tower having the most blocks. The students could also estimate and count specific blocks. Ask questions like, *How many triangle blocks did you use to build your castle?*

Sometime when the children are lining up blocks, encourage them to line the blocks up like dominoes and then knock them over by tipping the first block. Ask the children how many blocks they have lined up. Have them guess first, then count and record their answer. Challenge them to top that number the next time.

Spots on a Leopard

LITERATURE CONNECTION

Read *How Many Spots Does a Leopard Have?* by Julius Lester (Scholastic, 1989). This is a funny African story that makes children who have learned to count feel good. Each child can then draw a leopard, having no more spots than he or she can count. Each artist can write on the back of a picture the number of spots he or she drew, and others can count the spots, then peek at the back to see if they agree.

Older primary students might make these pictures, drawing the dots in two colors. The children could then write an equation on the back corresponding to the dots; for example, 4 red + 3 blue = 7 spots on my leopard. Other students could then check the equation to see if they agree with it or not.

Active Math Games

PHYSICAL EDUCATION CONNECTION

Games give a wonderful opportunity for children to learn math kinesthetically. These two activities progress in difficulty from an easier to a harder one.

- Play Mother, May I? on the playground. Everyone stands in a line opposite the Mother, who calls on children to take a certain number of steps toward her. She tells how many steps and what kind of steps (giant or baby) the child may take; for example, "Derek, you may take three giant steps forward." Before moving, the child must remember to say, "Mother, may I?" The goal is to reach the Mother.

- Sing the song "Go In and Out the Window" with the children as they stand in a circle with their arms raised to form windows. Choose five children to go in and out the windows. When the song ends, close the windows (hands come down) and say together how many children are inside and how many are outside the circle.

After a while, change the number of children to six, seven, or eight. For older children, have the class call out an equation: Three inside plus four outside equals seven in all.

Treehouse

TECHNOLOGY CONNECTION

The Treehouse, Broderbund
Apple II Series, Macintosh, IBM/Compatible

To reinforce and apply what the children have learned about coin values, show them how to select the Road Rally Game by clicking on the game at the bottom of the screen inside the treehouse.

A child may choose the Money Game setting and play this game with a friend. They could start with the 50¢ game goal, the easiest level. They click on the ? to roll the die. To move the car the number of spaces indicated on the die, they click on the game board. Children earn or lose money in the game and have to choose which set of coins represents more money. Play continues until players reach the goal.

The treehouse is full of other surprises, such as a Treehouse Theater, and making music, and playing instruments in the orchestra.

Marvelous Math Music

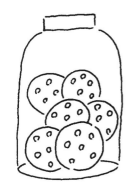

MUSIC CONNECTION

 These two music activities help children learn the order of numbers and counting, using groups of tens and ones.

■ Who Stole the Cookies from the Cookie Jar?

For number ordering, try this call-and-response song:

Who stole the cookies from the cookie jar? Number 1 stole the cookies from the cookie jar?

Who, me?
Yes, you!
Couldn't be!
Then who?
Number 2 stole the cookies. . .

To help with number recognition, give ten children cards, numbered one to ten. The first ten, as their number-names are cleared, can give their cards to others who have not yet been accused. If the game were to end with, No one stole the cookies . . . , you could pass the cookie jar.

■ Sing a Song of Sixpence

Teach the children the musical nursery rhyme "Sing a Song of Sixpence." Talk about the number of blackbirds in the song. The children can model the "four-and-twenty blackbirds" by grouping themselves into tens and ones.

Let the children suggest other numbers of blackbirds they can model, and change the number of blackbirds in the song, each time having the children show the number as tens and ones.

The Counting House

LITERATURE CONNECTION

 Anno's Counting House by Mitsumasa Anno (Philomel Books, 1982) is a wordless book about ten children who move one-by-one from one house to another.

There are some ideas suggested by the author at the beginning of the book for ways for children to dramatize the story.

In addition, the class might model the story using counters and outlines of houses drawn on paper. Read the story aloud and as you do, have the children move their counters from one house to the other, just as the children in the story move. Then your students could write the different number combinations for ten.

Let's Play Store

DRAMATIC PLAY CONNECTION

 To reinforce the concept of counting using groups of tens and ones, set up a store in your play area. Provide the students with a cash register, play-money, paper bags, boxes, and items from around the classroom, such as math manipulatives, puppets, plastic play food, paper, pencils, crayons, paper clips, etc.

Put out some real catalogs or some that you and the children have made. (You can make catalogs by using photos from educational supply catalogs, gift catalogs, or supermarket sales flyers. You and the students could add some prices geared to the amounts of money the children are using.)

The children can use the play money to buy and sell things from the catalogs. Some children can be shoppers and others store clerks. The clerks can also use boxes and bags to group the items on the shelves in cartons and in packages of ten.

Groups-of-Ten Art

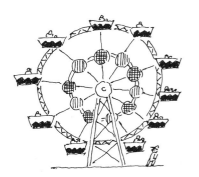

ART CONNECTION

Introduce this activity by drawing the children's attention to the classroom American flag. Give each child a picture of the flag, and have them count the number of stars on it by circling each group of ten stars.

Share with the class the book *Anno's USA* by Mitsumasa Anno (Philomel Books, 1983). Have the children draw their own pictures containing groups of ten objects. Alternatively, they might create collages of groups of ten objects like cut-out stars, beans, split peas, macaroni, or buttons, using heavy paper and glue.

The pictures might be made into a bulletin board display or a class book. As the children look at one another's pictures, you can challenge them to count by tens to tell the total number of objects pictured without counting every object.

You might want to stage an art show of the completed pictures or collages. Group them by total value, that is, all of the artwork having ten objects in one section of the classroom and that having twenty objects in another. By grouping like totals together the students will see many different representations of the same number.

Equation Stories

LANGUAGE ARTS CONNECTION

 To prepare for this activity, write simple equations (such as 2 + 4 = 6) on slips of paper and put enough of them in a box so there is one for each student.

Say to the class, *Let's write a sample story together.* Draw an equation from the box and write it at the top of a piece of chart paper as a title. Read the story shown to get the children's imaginations going, then let them create a story that goes with the equation you drew. Write it on the chart paper.

Then say, *Now you get to draw your own equation from the box and write your own story.* You may want to have the children brainstorm a list of topics to help them get started. When finished, you can group the stories into Math Magazines.

At the end of each day, choose one or two children to read their stories, omitting the headlines (equations). After the class has heard the story have them try to tell the headline (equation) that belongs with it.

7 + 5 = 12

Last week, a spaceship landed in our playground. First 7 green creatures came out. Soon 5 more creatures appeared. The 12 creatures disappeared. They might be hiding in town somewhere!

Cooking Equations

COOKING CONNECTION

Provide undecorated cookies, frosting, and two kinds of cookie decorations (raisins and chocolate chips, for example). Choose a Decoration Number (a number between five and ten) and have each child "order" a cookie.

After the children have written their names on pieces of paper, they should write the number of raisins and the number of chocolate chips that they want on their cookie. Have each child check that the sum of these two numbers equals the specified Decoration Number.

These orders then go to the Cooks, who prepare each cookie order and deliver it on a paper towel or napkin to the child who ordered it.

Older children can each draw a picture of their cookie and the equation that it represents.

NUMBER RELATIONS LITERATURE LIST

Aker, Suzanne. *What Comes in 2's, 3's, and 4's?* New York: Simon and Schuster Books for Young Readers, 1990.

Anno, Mitsumasa. *Anno's Counting Book.* New York: Harper Junior Books, 1986.

_____. *Anno's Counting House.* New York: Philomel Books, 1982.

_____. *Anno's Mysterious Multiplying Jar.* New York: Putnam, 1983.

_____. *Anno's USA.* New York: Philomel Books, 1983.

Dee, Ruby. *Two Ways to Count to Ten.* New York: Henry Holt and Co. Inc., 1988.

Ehlert, Lois. *Fish Eyes.* San Diego, CA: Harcourt Brace Jovanovich, 1990.

Feelings, Muriel. *Moja Means One: The Swahili Counting Book.* New York: The Dial Press, 1971.

Fisher, Leonard E. *Number Art: Thirteen 123s from Around the World.* New York: Four Winds, 1982.

Grossman, Virginia, and Sylvia Long. *Ten Little Rabbits.* San Francisco, CA: Chronicle Books, 1991.

Hamm, Diane Johnston. *How Many Feet in the Bed?* New York: Simon and Schuster Books for Young Readers, 1991.

Hutchins, Pat. *The Doorbell Rang.* New York: Greenwillow Books, 1986.

Lester, Julius. *How Many Spots Does a Leopard Have?* New York: Scholastic, 1989.

Lindbergh, Reeve. *The Midnight Farm.* New York: Dial Books for Young Readers, 1987.

MacCarthy, Patricia. *Ocean Parade.* New York: Dial Books for Young Readers, 1990.

Mathis, Sharon B. *The Hundred-Penny Box.* New York: Penguin, 1986.

Nuffield Math Project. *Math Begins.* The Nuffield Foundation.

Rees, Mary. *Ten in a Bed.* Boston, MA: Little, Brown, 1988.

Schwartz, David. *How Much Is a Million?* New York: Scholastic, 1987.

Viorst, Judith. *Alexander, Who Used to Be Rich Last Sunday.* New York: Atheneum, 1978.

Patterns and Relationships

SURROUNDED BY PATTERN

Children love exploring the wonderful world of patterns. In mathematics, patterns form the underlying structure that enables us to make sense of numbers and their relationships. Patterns are predictable, reliable sequences or series of events, and the ability to identify and extend patterns is an invaluable resource for solving many problems.

In order to use mathematical patterns as a problem-solving tool, children must first learn to recognize patterns. The activities in this section give them practice in recognizing and extending patterns in many different curriculum areas.

What do the experts say?

Patterns help us understand our world; they help us anticipate the next step rather than our experiencing each step as a new and isolated phenomenon.

Mary Baratta-Lorton
Mathematics Their Way

Rhythmic Patterns

MUSIC CONNECTION

 Here are some different ideas for ways to bring pattern into the classroom with music.

- To create sound and rhythmic patterns, have the children use classroom percussion instruments, or tap on cans, crash together pot lids, and shake plastic jars filled with dried beans. For a pattern children can both see and hear, arrange the instruments in a pattern, then have the children play them in order. Record the pattern on chart paper by writing the pattern of sounds.

- Try some repeating rhythm patterns together. Begin the pattern yourself, clapping or with an instrument, and have the children join in as they catch on.

- You can also make patterns based upon where you hold the instrument when you strike it, for example, over your head, behind your back, over your head, behind your back, etc. Children love doing this activity as they march around the room to music.

- Children enjoy exploring numbers through sound. Gather the children on the floor with some percussion instruments. Together choose a number. As each child, in turn, plays that many beats in a pattern on an instrument, lead the other children in clapping to mimic that pattern. For example, beat and clap the number five as fast, fast, slow, slow, slow; or slow, fast, slow, fast, slow.

Patterns in Nature

SCIENCE CONNECTION

Use *Spirals, Curves, Fanshapes and Lines* by Tana Hoban (Greenwillow Books, 1992) to introduce students to the idea of patterns in nature. Rich photographs, such as the spiral of a nautilus shell, show children some of the different patterns that can be found in nature.

Then take the children on a nature walk. Before the walk, talk about the importance of preserving our natural surroundings. Discuss what patterns they might find. They might look for flowers, spider webs, animal coats, shells, and rocks, possibly snowflakes, honeycombs, or rainbows.

Instead of bringing back to class real examples of patterns in nature, have the children make color sketches of the things they noticed on their walk. These can be grouped together by type of pattern to form a class book.

Mosaic Magic

TECHNOLOGY CONNECTION

Mosaic Magic, Kinder Magic Software
Macintosh, IBM/Compatible

Children can discover and complete patterns by playing the computer game, *Tattle Tiles*. Demonstrate to the children how to access the game by clicking on the words *Tattle Tiles* from the *Main Menu*. Help them choose the appropriate level, perhaps beginning at the basic level, *Medal Chase*. A 10-x-10 grid will appear on the screen with a picture pattern containing one or more smiling stars.

The children choose the tile they think belongs in the star by first clicking on a color or shape, and then clicking on the star in the grid. As individuals work, ask, *What pattern are you trying to complete? How can you tell it is a pattern?*

The children could transfer the designs to one-inch graph paper and display them around the classroom.

Pattern Necklaces

ART CONNECTION

Designing necklaces gives children some opportunities to create their own patterns. Both the creation of the beads themselves and the stringing of the beads in patterns will offer learning experiences.

The students can shape beads from clay or from flour, salt, and water dough, and then paint them. The children can use yarn or string to make the necklace itself. See *The Incredible Clay Book* by Sherri Haab and Laura Torres (Klutz Press, 1994) for specific ideas for bead designs.

These necklaces, while giving the children practice with creating patterns, also make great gifts to take home.

Predictable Pattern Books

LITERATURE CONNECTION

 Many children's books have predictable patterns of text. These books make excellent choices for beginning readers. Children delight in these books and get the feeling of really being able to read.

Gather the children in a learning circle, and read the book *Brown Bear, Brown Bear, What Do You See?* (Henry Holt, 1983). On the second reading, or as soon as they have identified the pattern, have the students join in.

Let's make up our own story of Brown Bear. Everyone think of one animal to add, and what color it will be. Begin the story. *Brown bear, brown bear, what do you see? I see a . . .* Point to the first child in the circle to fill in the blank (grey whale, for instance), and then continue with the pattern. The children should chant along, stopping only for the next animal to be added, until every child has had a chance to contribute.

(Other books having predictable patterns are included in the literature list at the end of this section.)

Woven Bracelets

ART CONNECTION

 Weaving is a wonderful activity; it teaches about patterns while creating a keepsake. You might introduce this activity by using the book *Ten Little Rabbits* by Virginia Grossman and Sylvia Long (Chronicle Books, 1991).

Another way to introduce this activity is kinesthetically by asking for three volunteers. Have them lie parallel to each other on the floor, and then begin to weave them, using big, thick yarn. As you do this explain what you are doing: *On the first row, I'm going over the first person, under the second, and over the third. But on the second row, I'm doing the opposite; I'm going under the first, over the second, and under the third.* Then have the students tell you how to weave the third row.

Provide each student with a piece of thick cardboard (3 inches × 4 inches). Make three one-half-inch cuts in both of the three-inch ends. Wrap three rubber bands lengthwise around the cardboard sliding them through the cuts at each end.

Provide the children with yarn, (multicolored works particularly nicely) and have them weave over, under, over on one row, and then under, over, under on the next. Have them complete one side of the weaving and then continue right on to the other side. When finished, knot the end of the yarn and have the student remove her or his very own woven bracelet. Many children will want to make more than one.

Edible Patterns

COOKING CONNECTION

Here are some ideas for bringing pattern into the classroom with cooking.

■ Pattern Sticks

Try this variation of the ants-on-a-log theme. Set out celery sticks, raisins, nuts, and cream cheese or peanut butter. Have the children make pattern sticks for themselves by spreading sticks of celery with cream cheese (or peanut butter) and then arranging the nuts and raisins on them to make a pattern.

■ Gingerbread Houses

Making Gingerbread Houses is another good cooking project involving patterns. Make the houses by covering milk cartons with icing and graham crackers. Set out gum drops, peanuts, chocolate chips, and other decorations. The children can arrange these decorations in a pattern on the houses.

Afterwards have the children describe their patterns as they eat their concoctions.

Making Patterns Using Our Bodies

PHYSICAL EDUCATION CONNECTION

 These are ideas for bringing motion patterns into the classroom.

■ Start a motion pattern, arms up, arms down, arms up, arms down, for instance. Say, *Join in when you know the pattern. Can anyone describe our pattern with words?* Once the pattern has been translated into words in several ways, say, *Let's try the same pattern again, but with different motions. Does anyone have an idea for new motions we could try?* Keep each pattern going until everyone joins in. Then have the children translate the pattern into words.

■ Gather in a circle to do "The Hokey Pokey." The first verse, *You put your right hand in, You put your right hand out, You put your right hand in, and you shake it all about. You do the hokey pokey, and you turn yourself around; That's what it's all about!* is followed by left hand, right foot, left foot, and so on.

■ Children love to create and perform body movement patterns. Gather in a circle on the rug. Talk about making body patterns by standing, crouching, or sitting in different positions, such as facing forward or backward. *Let's make this pattern: Stand, stand, sit, sit, stand, stand, sit, sit.* As you tap the head of each child, the child should take the position that comes next in the pattern. When everyone is in position, "read" the pattern chorally around the circle. Try a variety of these position patterns with the children.

Help Tell a Story

MULTICULTURAL CONNECTION

 The story *The Old Woman and the Red Pumpkin,* Betsy Bang (Macmillan, 1975), retells a Bengali folk tale that features several memorable patterns, in both structure and language.

At the outset invite the children to join in as soon as they think they know what you're going to say next. "Tok-tok" will probably be their first venture. At the point where the bear appears, pause. If no one offers "Ury bop, and old woman!" continue, emphasizing it yourself.

Do this throughout the story, moving quickly through the narrative, but giving the children a chance to precede you on the repetitive patterns. A second reading will give the class confidence, and, after that, dramatic play is in order.

The illustrator, Molly Garrett Bang, provides hidden Bengali calligraphy in the accompanying pictures.

Creating Patterns

ART CONNECTION

 Your class might enjoy doing one or more of these pattern activities in moments of creativity.

- The children can make their own pattern stamps from pieces of sponge that you have cut into interesting shapes. Set up separate stations for each color of paint and provide different shapes at each station. Encourage the children to take a little time to plan their patterns before stamping away.

- Have students create patterns with layers of colored sand in empty baby food jars with lids. Give the students wooden popsicle sticks so they can gently move the sand into position. You might suggest that the children draw their pattern on a sheet of paper before actually beginning.

- Provide students at the sand table with shells or cookie cutters. Encourage them to make patterns in the sand by making imprints with the different shells or cutters. Watch the children as they work and ask questions like, *What shell would you use next in your pattern?*

PATTERNS AND RELATIONSHIPS
LITERATURE LIST

Bang, Betsy. *The Old Woman and the Red Pumpkin*. New York: Macmillan, 1975.

Baratta-Lorton, Mary. *Mathematics Their Way*. Menlo Park, CA: Addison-Wesley, 1976.

Campbell, Rod. *Dear Zoo*. New York: Four Winds Press, 1982.

Carle, Eric. *The Grouchy Ladybug*. New York: Harper Trophy Picture Books, 1986.

_____. *The Very Busy Spider*. New York: Philomel Books, 1989.

Fox, Mem. *Hattie and the Fox*. New York: Bradbury Press, 1988.

Grossman, Virginia, and Sylvia Long. *Ten Little Rabbits*. San Francisco, CA: Chronicle Books, 1991.

Haab, Sherri, and Laura Torres. *The Incredible Clay Book*. Palo Alto, CA: Klutz Press, 1994.

Hoban, Tana. *Spirals, Curves, Fanshapes and Lines*. New York: Greenwillow Books, 1992.

Hutchins, Pat. *Don't Forget the Bacon*. New York: Morrow, 1989.

Martin, Jr., Bill. *Brown Bear, Brown Bear, What Do You See?* New York: Henry Holt and Company, 1983.

McLean, Anne. *The Bus Ride*. Glenview, IL: Scott, Foresman, 1971.

Morgan, Pierr. *The Turnip*. New York: Philomel Books, 1990.

Parks, Brenda. *Who's in the Shed?* Crystal Lake, IL: Rigby Education, 1986.

Polacco, Patricia. *Rechenka's Eggs*. New York: Putnam, 1988.

Rosen, Michael. *We're Going on a Bear Hunt*. New York: McElderry Books, 1989.

Ward, Cindy. *Cookie's Week*. New York: Scholastic, 1988.

Wood, Audrey. *The Napping House*. San Diego, CA: Harcourt, Brace, Jovanovich, 1984.

Yarbrough, Camille. *Cornrows*. New York: Putnam, 1988.

Zemach, Margot. *The Little Red Hen: An Old Story*. New York: Farrar, Straus and Giroux, 1983.

Data Analysis

COLLECTING, COMMUNICATING, AND INTERPRETING DATA

Data collection and analysis are skills that adults frequently use to learn about the world and to help make decisions. The activities in this section introduce children to the concepts of making observations, sequencing events, and organizing and analyzing collected data. As the children progress, they will learn to make up questions that are interesting to them, find ways to answer them, and begin trying to communicate their thoughts in writing.

By collecting data about themselves and the world close to them, we pique their curiosity. How many paper clips can one of their hairs hold before it snaps? How tall will their seed grow in one week? How do their classmates get to school? What do they like on their spaghetti? These are authentic questions that automatically engage children.

What do the experts say?

A developmentally appropriate curriculum encourages the exploration of a wide variety of mathematical ideas in such a way that children retain their enjoyment of, and curiosity about, mathematics. It incorporates real-world contexts, children's experiences, and children's language in developing ideas. It recognizes that children need considerable time to construct sound understandings and develop the ability to reason and communicate mathematically.

National Council of Teachers of Mathematics
Curriculum and Evaluation Standards for School Mathematics

Seed Studies

SCIENCE CONNECTION

Bring in different kinds of fruits and let the children guess, then count, how many seeds are in each. Include fruits that have lots of seeds, such as watermelons and cantaloupes, as well as fruits that have only a few or just one seed, such as peaches and plums.

Make a chart or graph showing just how many seeds each fruit had. Ask the children for ideas on how to group the information and how to show their findings. End the project by making, and eating, a delicious fruit salad.

Sunflowers are wonderful for estimation and counting activities. Have the children guess how many seeds there are in the sunflower. Then remove the seeds and have the students count them. You could do this with several sunflowers, and then have the class show on a picture graph the number of seeds they found in each one.

Me Collages

ART CONNECTION

 Hold a class discussion about the students' favorite colors, toys, sports, books, animals, and so forth. Then provide students with a wide variety of magazines that they may cut up. Toy catalogs and nature magazines are good choices.

Have each child clip pictures of favorite things and arrange them to create a collage. Let the children draw a picture of a favorite thing if they cannot find a picture of it. Have the children sign their names on the back of their art work.

Hold an art show of the students' collages. Ask questions like these to get a discussion going:

- Using the data in each collage, can you identify the artist?
- Looking at all of the collages, what can you say about the children in this class?
- What are the most-favorite things for this class?

Birthday Bonanza

MUSIC CONNECTION

 To gather data on the students' birthday months, sing the following song all together, to the tune of "London Bridge is Falling Down."

Apples, peaches, pears, and plums,
Pears and plums,
Pears and plums;
Tell us when your birthday comes,
Bob — by Jones.

As you sing the last line of the song (a student's first and last name), point to that student and have that child name the month of her or his birthday. Then sing the song again, using another child's name.

After singing the song to find out and note everyone's birthday month, make a graph to show the data. Draw vertical lines on chart paper to create twelve columns. With the children watching, write the months of the year at the bottom of each column. Then have the children write their names and birth months on small squares of paper. Let each child tape a paper in the appropriate month's column.

As a group, analyze the results:

■ Which month has the most birthdays?
■ Which month has the fewest?
■ Which month has the same number of birthdays as August (or any month you name)?

Hair-Strength Testing

SCIENCE CONNECTION

This activity gives the children an opportunity to gather data and draw conclusions.

Divide the class into groups and pull or cut a hair from the head of several children in each group. (Pick children who are willing to have a hair pulled and who have fairly long hair.) Have the students tie each hair on a paper clip, helping them when necessary. Tape each hair to the edge of a table letting the clip hang down.

Then have the students add paper clips, in a chain, to the first paper clip. Have them find out how many paper clips they can add before their hair snaps.

Have each group of students write their names and the number of paper clips their hairs can hold on a class chart. Then have a class discussion as follows:

- What type of hair seems to be the strongest? Which seems weakest?
- What other information can we gather about the students' hairs?
- What conclusions can you draw from your data?
- If you did this experiment again with the same hair, do you think it would hold exactly the same number of paper clips? Why or why not?

Cooking with Strega Nona

LITERATURE CONNECTION

 Begin by reading *Strega Nona* by Tomie de Paola (Prentice Hall, 1975) to the class. Then make a large chart having six columns. Mark each column with the children's choices of a sauce for spaghetti: Plain, Butter, Cheese, Butter and Cheese, Spaghetti Sauce, Spaghetti Sauce and Cheese.

Have the children write their names on small pieces of paper and put them in the appropriate columns on the chart to show how they like their spaghetti. Have the children count how many servings of each choice are needed.

With some outside help, cook enough spaghetti so each child can have some. Prepare the sauces and top each serving with the correct sauce. Have some of the children serve the others. Bon appetite!

As they are eating, the children might discuss their spaghetti sauce graph. Here are some questions to start with:

- Which choice was the most popular? Which was the second most popular?
- Which was the least popular?
- Which choices did the same number of children request?
- Which choice do you think Strega Nona would have made?

Favorite Foods, Healthy Foods

SCIENCE CONNECTION

 Discuss the children's favorite foods with them and make a list of the foods on the chalkboard. Then compare these foods with those in the food pyramid being promoted by nutrition experts. Note where each kind of food fits in the pyramid. Ask, *Which foods are considered healthy, and which should be limited?*

Have the children make drawings of the food pyramid, putting their own special foods in the correct places, if possible. You might help them to make lists or tallies of healthy and unhealthy foods.

You could extend this activity into Social Studies by investigating where the children's favorite foods originated. Work together as a class to locate these various places on a world map. Make small paper labels each having the name of a favorite food, and use pins to stick the labels on the map in the appropriate locations.

Transportation Tally

SOCIAL STUDIES CONNECTION

 Have your students discuss the different ways that they get to school. Divide a big sheet of chart paper with horizontal lines. Label each row with a different transportation method the children use; for example, bus, walking, bicycle, car.

Younger children could then write their names in the appropriate rows. Older children might make tallies. Show them how to cross the first four tally marks to make five, making it easier to count the results. Then discuss the results:

- How do most of you get to school?
- What is the difference between the number of you who walk to school and the number who ride the bus?
- How do you think most children in this county, or city, get to school?
- Do you think their chart would be different from ours? Why or why not?

Plant Growth

SCIENCE CONNECTION

 Plant a seed and then take photographs of the small growing plant every few days. The children can put the photographs in order in a photo album that chronicles the life of the plant from a tiny seed to adult. Or they can plant their own seeds and keep diaries in which they draw pictures to show how their plants change and grow. For kinesthetic learners, acting out the growth of seeds is an especially effective learning activity. The teacher can guide this activity with words and motions like the following:

There is a little seed and the farmer has planted it in the ground.
   (Crouch in a ball, low to the ground.)

The sun has warmed it and the rain has watered it. It starts to grow roots down into the dirt.
   (Unfold a leg.)

It starts to grow a stem.
   (Move arm upwards and begin to stand.)

It sprouts some leaves.
   (Move arms outwards and continue to stand.)

And then a big flower blooms.
   (Lift up head.)

From the flower, a tiny seed drops to the ground.
   (Drop to the ground in a ball position again.)

The cycle begins again!

Books that you might use with this activity are:
From Seed to Plant by Gail Gibbons (Holiday House, 1991)
How Things Grow by Peter Seymour (E.P. Dutton, 1988)
The Carrot Seed by Ruth Krauss (Harper and Row, 1945)

Curious Classmates

LANGUAGE ARTS CONNECTION

Talk to the class about conducting interviews. Decide upon the questions that the children would like to ask each other. They might concern favorites, such as their favorite colors, board games, and stories.

Then have the children draw names to find out which classmate they are to interview. After conducting the interview, help them write a few words or use rebus pictures to tell about their class-mates' favorites.

You could provide a survey form for the children to fill out during their interview. Then you might adapt the form for younger children by using pictures or multiple choices for them to circle.

A sample interview form follows:

Your name: _____

Name of person that you are interviewing:

_____

Favorite color: _____

Favorite game: _____

Favorite book: _____

Favorite food: _____

Favorite pet: _____

Favorite song: _____

Favorite _____ : _____

After the children have interviewed each other, let them decide how to display their information.

From Sheep to Sweater

SOCIAL STUDIES CONNECTION

Begin a class discussion by asking the students how they think some of their clothes were made. After different ideas have been tossed about, read *Pelle's New Suit* by Elsa Beskow (Floris Books, 1989).

The book shows the steps involved in making a boy's suit, beginning with shearing of the sheep, all the way to the sewing of the suit. Make cards using pictures that show the different steps that are involved. Let the children arrange them in sequence.

If possible have someone who spins or weaves wool come to class to demonstrate and explain the craft.

DATA ANALYSIS LITERATURE LIST

Beskow, Elsa. *Pelle's New Suit*. New York: Harper and Row, 1929; (Floris Books, 1989).

de Paola, Tomie. *Strega Nona*. Englewood Cliffs, NJ: Prentice Hall, 1975.

Frasier, Debra. *On the Day You Were Born*. San Diego, CA: Harcourt, Brace, Jovanovich, 1991.

Gibbons, Gail. *From Seed to Plant*. New York: Holiday House, 1991.

Krauss, Ruth. *The Carrot Seed*. New York: Harper and Row, 1945.

National Council of Teachers of Mathematics. *Curriculum and Evaluation Standards for School Mathematics*. Reston, VA: The Council, 1989.

Sendak, Maurice. *Chicken Soup with Rice*. New York: Harper and Row, 1962.

Seymour, Peter. *How Things Grow*. New York: E.P. Dutton, 1988.

Stone, Antonia, and Susan Jo Russell. *Used Numbers, Counting: Ourselves and Our Family*. Palo Alto, CA: Dale Seymour Publications, 1990.

Geometry and Visual Thinking

THE RICH WORLD OF SHAPE

The activities in this section give children many opportunities to investigate, experiment with, and explore geometric shapes by interacting with everyday objects and physical materials. From a child's first shape-sorter toy to a later fascination with puzzles, children seem to be drawn to activities that exercise their spatial abilities.

Visualization is a strategy that goes hand in hand with geometric explorations. Children's visual skills are challenged as they create intricate designs by tracing and rotating shapes, construct sculptures with wood scraps, build structures with toothpicks and clay, and design artwork using geometric shapes. Children are naturally drawn to these activities and find the materials intriguing and motivating.

What do the experts say?

Spatial sense is an intuitive feel for one's surroundings and the objects in them. To develop spatial sense, children must have many experiences that focus on geometric relationships; the direction, orientation, and perspectives of objects in space; the relative shapes and sizes of figures and objects; and how a change in shape relates to a change in size.

National Council of Teachers of Mathematics
Curriculum and Evaluation Standards for School Mathematics

Stamping Shapes

ART CONNECTION

 Set out sponges cut into different geometric shapes (circle, square, triangle, oval, for example), along with some paint in shallow containers, paint brushes, and a supply of paper.

Show the children how they can use shape sponges to print a picture or a scene on paper. The square and the triangle, for instance, can be used to make a house. The children can add details with paintbrushes.

Talk with the children as they work. Ask them questions such as:

- Tell me about your picture. What are the different shapes you've used so far?
- How are you putting different shapes together to make pictures of some things?

Kid Pix

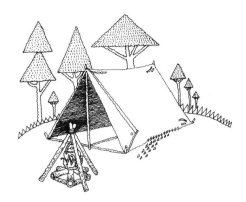

TECHNOLOGY CONNECTION

Kid Pix, Broderbund
IBM/Compatible, Macintosh (English, Spanish on both)

Children can draw various three-sided and four-sided geometric shapes using the computer. As they draw these shapes, show them how to draw a straight horizontal, vertical, or 45-degree angle line by pressing the Shift key while using the line tool. Encourage the children to experiment and draw a variety of shapes and sizes. They may even want to draw them in some kind of pattern. Discuss the shapes with them using questions like:

- What kinds of shapes can you find?
- Which ones can you name?
- Which shapes look like Pattern Blocks?

The children could print and display the shapes in the classroom or make a class book of shapes.

Shape Sandwiches

COOKING CONNECTION

 Bring to the classroom as many cookie cutters in different geometric shapes as possible. Also provide bread (thin slices are best) and a spread or two for the bread (peanut butter, cream cheese, jam).

Have the children use the cookie cutters to cut the bread into shapes for making little sandwiches. As the children are preparing their sandwiches, ask them questions like the following:

- What shapes did you choose? What are their names?
- Which shape would make the biggest sandwich? The smallest?
- What shapes could you put together to make a design?

The children might want to make a couple of sandwiches and arrange them in a design. For example, an oval and a triangle might form a fish, or four triangles can create a pinwheel. Encourage the children to experiment and to let their imaginations loose.

Anansi the Spider

MULTICULTURAL CONNECTION

 Gerald McDermott's *Anansi the Spider* (Holt, Rinehart and Winston, 1972) is an African tale in which each of a group of characters has one miraculous physical attribute. This simple retelling of the story is a good introduction to a major African cultural hero and an excellent vehicle for creative dramatics.

McDermott's illustrations use distinctive shapes to identify each of the characters in the story. As you read the story to the children, point out the characters' distinctive identifying shapes. You might make large cutouts of these shapes to use as identifiers, pinned to the clothes of the child playing each role, as you read the drama aloud.

This is a play that can stand many repetitions, using different casts. Let each cast create its own interpretation. Be sure to let each Sky God choose his or her own method of taking the moon to the sky, which can be a very dramatic scene.

Scrap Sculptures

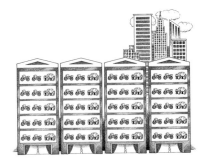

GAMES/CREATIVITY CONNECTION

 Set out some white glue and a supply of wood scraps for the children to work with. Say, *Let's make some wood sculptures. Build something with the wood scraps and then join the pieces of wood together with glue.*

As the children work, talk with them about what they are building and help them notice the shapes of the wood scraps they are using. Call attention to shape by asking questions like these:

- What are you building?
- Do you see any shapes you can name in your sculpture?
- What do the shapes remind you of?

In a day or two, after the sculptures have dried, the children may wish to paint them.

Shape Poems

LANGUAGE ARTS CONNECTION

Talk with your children about creating shape poems. Tell them that this is done by choosing a shape that they would like to tell about, and then writing words about it so that they form the shape being described.

See the example below for a poem about circles. A poem about triangles could be written so that the words outline the shape of a triangle, or so that the words fill a triangular space on the page.

If the children are too young to write poems by themselves, the class could create some group efforts, with you writing the words on the chalkboard or chart paper. The children could then illustrate their poems.

Balloons against the sun, a full moon rolling a ball to his mother, a clown's nose. reflected in the lake, a baby in the lake, a baby rolling a ball to his mother, a clown's nose.

Getting into Shape

PHYSICAL EDUCATION CONNECTION

 Here are some ways the children can make shapes with their bodies, either as a group, by themselves, or with a partner.

■ Make some big shapes. Have the children stand up and join hands. Suggest a shape to start with, and have the group try to form itself into that shape. For example, say, *Let's work together to form a circle. What's a circle like?*

■ Then try to form a square. *What do you know about a square? How is it different from the circle we've just made? How can we change our circle into a square?*

■ Next try having the children work alone or with a partner. *Let's use our bodies to make shapes on the floor.* Have each child or pair select a shape and practice making it by standing or lying down to form the outline of the shape.

After a practice time, call the class back together and have one pair at a time perform their shape skit. The class members should try to name each shape as others make it. Stimulate discussion by asking questions such as:

■ Can you tell what this shape is? How did you know?

■ How many sides does this shape have?

■ Does this shape have any corners? How many are there?

■ What shapes are alike? Which are different?

Shapes, Shapes, Shapes

LITERATURE CONNECTION

Tana Hoban's book *Shapes, Shapes, Shapes* (Greenwillow, 1996) is full of rich and wonderful photographs. Introduce the book to the children by telling them it is a book that has some amazing pictures in it. Say, *There is so much to notice! Let's see how good you are at spotting shapes.*

Share the book with the children, giving them time to examine each page in detail. As children spot shapes in each photograph, have them tell about what they have found. Keep discussion going with questions and comments like these:

- What shape have you noticed?
- Where it is in the photograph? Can you point it out for us?
- Are there any others like it on the page? Let's count them together.
- No one has noticed a circle yet in this picture. Are there any?
- What shape do you see the most of on this page?

After you have read and discussed the book, provide the children with pieces of colored paper that have been cut in various shapes. (Sometimes you can find paper having a gummed back.) Have the children create their own pictures using the theme "shapes, shapes, shapes."

Toothpick and Clay Sculptures

ART CONNECTION

 Building structures with toothpicks and clay gives children the opportunity to explore shapes in a new, and kinesthetic, way. Using small clay balls as connectors for the toothpicks, the children can build structures of various shapes and sizes.

Encourage the class to start with some easy, two-dimensional shapes like squares or triangles. Later, the children may want to try three-dimensional shapes like cubes or prisms. You may want to provide some examples to start them off. As the children build, have them pay attention to which shapes seem easiest to build and which ones seem strongest.

You could use tiny marshmallows, peas, or gumdrops as connectors, instead of clay, if you wish.

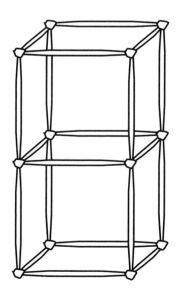

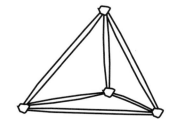

Twister Designs

TECHNOLOGY CONNECTION

Thinkin' Things, Edmark
MS-DOS, Macintosh

Twister Designs are created by hand by 1) cutting a shape out of tag board; 2) poking a push pin through the center of the shape, a piece of paper, and then a piece of cardboard; 3) tracing around the shape; and 4) rotating the shape and tracing around it again. The designer repeats the process until reaching the starting point again.

Children will delight in making their own Twister Designs on the computer as they explore the world of geometric shapes, motion, and sound. Children select the *BLOX-Flying Shapes* module. They can grab a shape by clicking and holding the center of the shape and then moving the mouse.

To rotate a shape, children click and hold the point of the shape, then rotate it by moving the mouse. To erase a shape, they click and hold the shape and then drag it onto the button bar to erase it.

GEOMETRY AND VISUAL THINKING LITERATURE LIST

Barrett, Peter, and Barrett, Susan. *The Circle Sarah Drew.* Merrick, NY: Scroll Press, 1973.

Ehlert, Lois. *Circus.* New York: HarperCollins Publishers, 1992.

_____. *Color Farm.* New York: J.B. Lippincott, Co., 1990.

_____. *Color Zoo.* New York: J.B. Lippincott, Co., 1989.

Ernst, Lisa Campbell, and Lee. *The Tangram Magician.* New York: Harry N. Abrams, 1990.

Grifalconi, Ann. *The Village of Round and Square Houses.* Boston, MA: Little, Brown, 1986.

Hoban, Tana. *Circles, Triangles, and Squares.* New York: Macmillan Publishing Co., 1974.

_____. *Over, Under and Through and Other Special Concepts.* New York: Macmillan Publishing Co., 1973.

_____. *Shapes, Shapes, Shapes.* New York: Greenwillow Books, 1986.

McDermott, Gerald. *Anansi the Spider.* New York: Holt, Rinehart and Winston, 1972.

_____. *Arrow to the Sun: a Pueblo Indian Tale.* New York: Viking Press, 1974.

McMillan, Bruce. *Fire Engine Shapes.* New York: Lothrop, Lee and Shepard, 1988.

_____. *Mouse Views: What the Class Pet Saw.* New York: Holiday House, 1993.

National Council of Teachers of Mathematics. *Curriculum and Evaluation Standards for School Mathematics.* Reston, VA: The Council, 1989.

Paul, Ann Whitford. *Eight Hands Round.* New York: HarperCollins Publishers, 1991.

Reiss, John. *Shapes.* New York: Bradbury Press, 1974.

Testa, Fulvio. *If You Look Around You.* New York: Dial Books for Young Readers, 1983.

Tompert, Ann. *Grandfather Tang's Story.* New York: Crown Publishers, 1990.

Logic and Algebra

EXAMINING DIFFERENCES AND POSSIBILITIES

The activities in this section give students many opportunities to classify and sort objects. By sorting blocks and classifying collections of shells or rocks, children practice thinking logically.

Classification activities teach children to look for similarities and differences and to make groups based on attributes. The ability to do this enables them to view the world in simpler terms, so that it seems less chaotic and random.

Through their work in sorting things into groups, the children begin to develop confidence in their own thinking and reasoning. They taste the thrill of finding multiple solutions to problems. They work at becoming more articulate in describing likenesses and differences in order to communicate their ideas and solutions clearly to the people around them. The ability to think and express ourselves logically is important as our world becomes more complex.

What do the experts say?

The importance of sorting and classifying activities in children's mathematical development is critical. Through these activities children learn to think analytically and to express their thoughts clearly. Forming classes and dealing with the relationships within a class and among different classes encourages the growth of clear and logical thinking, which is the basis of good mathematical reasoning.

Mary Baratta-Lorton
Mathematics Their Way

Block Sorting

REFERENCE SKILLS CONNECTION

Present a problem to the class such as cleaning up the block corner. Where does everything go?

Tell the children that they are going to organize and make clear some type of information. You might say, *Let's think of a way we can put the blocks on the shelves so that all the blocks that are alike go together. Then we can label the shelves to show where each kind of block goes.*

Listen to the children's ideas for organizing the blocks. Talk about which are good ideas and which one they could use best in their classroom. For example, they may wish to trace around each type of block and use the tracings as labels for the shelves.

As the children are organizing the blocks and putting them away, engage them in conversations about the blocks — how they are alike and how they are different. Ask the class if they think their way of organization will make it easier to find the blocks they need the next time. Inquire how they might keep the blocks organized in this way in the future.

Category Collage

ART CONNECTION

 Tell your students that they are going to make a picture book. On each page they will show things that are alike in some way. Have each child, or group of children, pick a category, like furniture, clothing, toys, food, or cars, and make a book page showing pictures of things that belong in that category.

The children can either cut pictures from old magazines or draw the items on their page with markers or crayons. Assemble the pages into a class book. Some children may wish to contribute several pages to the book.

As the children are working, talk with them about their pages. Help them to write how their pictures are alike. Write a dictated caption on each page, if possible, like, "We cut out pictures of toys," or "My pictures are all of things you wear."

When the book is completed, leave it in the Book Corner for the children to read on their own.

What Did You Have for Dinner?

SCIENCE CONNECTION

Have a discussion with the class about the basic food types — breads, cereals, and grains; vegetables and fruits; fish, poultry, and meats; and dairy products.

Have the children draw a picture of what they had for dinner last night. Then have them bring their pictures to a circle, sitting on the floor. Going around the circle, discuss which categories each of the children's foods fit under.

Identify foods that fit in none of the four categories and decide what to do about them. Make a large chart listing the different foods that go in each category and hang it up in the classroom.

Setting Up a Clothing Store

DRAMATIC PLAY CONNECTION

 Set up the classroom dramatic play area as a clothing store, having clothing racks and hangers, a mirror, and some display shelves. If possible provide a cash register and some play money on a small table to serve as the check-out stand. Provide a collection of merchandise (shoes, clothing, hats, handbags, belts, and so on) and leave it unorganized.

Ask the children to think how they can arrange the things in their store so people can easily find what they want. Encourage them to come up with some logical arrangements and to give reasons for their form of organization.

When the store is set up, let some children be clerks and some be customers. As they play, encourage the children to describe things they are buying or selling and to ask and answer questions like the following:

- Where can I find short-sleeved shirts?
- What kinds of shoes do you have for sale?
- How are all the things on this rack alike?
- How are these two shirts different?

Nature Collections

SCIENCE CONNECTION

 Children need many opportunities to observe objects and create classifications before they are introduced to formal, scientific classifications.

Make available some collections of natural objects in the classroom so the children can examine them, perhaps under a magnifying glass. Tell the children to look for similarities and differences, and to sort the objects in as many different ways as they can.

Leaves, rocks, shells, and seeds are just a few of the many readily available science materials that children find fascinating to sort. You could also provide some items that are not natural, but make good sorting collections, like buttons, counters, blocks, or marbles.

As children sort and classify, ask them questions such as:

- How did you sort your rocks? Can you think of another way?
- Tell me how you sorted your leaves. Do you think I can figure out where this leaf should go?
- How many different ways did you sort these seeds? Can you sort them in four ways?

Game of Categories

LANGUAGE ARTS CONNECTION

 Gather your children in a circle to play a game of Category. Chant and have the children clap rhythmically as you name a category (*Category,* clap, clap, *animals,* clap, clap) and go around the circle, having each child name something that fits in that category (*lion,* clap, clap, *elephant,* clap, clap, *dog,* clap, clap, etc.). Keep the categories as broad as possible, especially to begin with.

A good activity to follow the Category Game is Category of the Day. Place a big piece of butcher paper on a table with crayons or markers nearby. Have the children choose a Category of the Day (big things, animals, red things, things to eat, toys, things that fly, things made of wood). Label the butcher paper with the category the class chooses.

Have the children think of things that fit into that category. They can draw some of their ideas on the paper. Ask various children to tell how their drawing fits the category.

Transportation Collage

SOCIAL STUDIES CONNECTION

 Work with the class to make a transportation collage. Label three large pieces of butcher paper: Land, Sea, and Sky. Have the children cut out from old magazines pictures that portray different forms of transportation, then paste the pictures on one of the three murals.

For example, a picture of an airplane would go on the Sky paper, and a truck on the Land chart. Have the students share experiences they have had with the different modes of transportation. Students having good imaginations could make up some types of transportation they think might exist in the future and draw pictures of them to add to the charts.

You can have the class make such collages for practically any other social studies topic, such as kinds of food or clothing around the world, animal habitats, or the shapes of houses.

Caps for Sale

LITERATURE CONNECTION

 The classic children's book *Caps for Sale* by Esphyr Slobodkina (HarperCollins Children's Books, 1947) is a story about a peddler and some monkey business that leads to stimulating sorting activities.

Before reading the story, make a cap for each child in the class out of construction paper or plain coffee filters colored with marking pens. Make caps in two sizes, three colors, and three different patterns: plain, polka-dotted, and striped.

Tell the children that they are going to act out the story as you read it aloud. They can use the caps as props. Choose one child to be the peddler, and the rest of the class can be the monkeys. The children will especially enjoy mimicking the monkeys' behavior.

Draw special attention to the cap sorting that goes on near the end of the story. Ask the children to think of other ways the peddler could sort the caps. Try some of the ways to sort in the classroom: by size, by color, and by pattern.

Depending upon your students' ages and abilities, you could get into some more sophisticated sorting, such as small red dotted caps as opposed to large blue striped caps, and so on.

Animal Sort

SCIENCE CONNECTION

 Bring to class some pictures of farm and zoo animals. You can often find some inexpensive posters of these animals to cut up. Spread the pictures out in the center of the circle of students.

Put two large overlapping yarn loops by the pictures to form a Venn diagram. Label one circle *Farm Animals* and the other *Zoo Animals.*

Have each child select an animal picture and place it in the appropriate space in the circles. If a child selects an animal that is found both on a farm and in the zoo, a Brahma bull, perhaps, ask the children where that picture might go. Help them to see that it belongs in the intersection of the two yarn circles.

Children seem to love this activity. You can leave the loops available to the students, so they can go on to other choices and then return to the Venn diagram again and again. If they are available, you can use animal figurines for the sorting, instead of pictures.

People Sort

SOCIAL STUDIES CONNECTION

With this activity, you can capitalize on your students' natural curiosity about their classmates.

Put two large yarn loops (not overlapping) on the floor to form a Venn diagram. Label one circle *Yes* and the other *No*. Give each child a small card with his or her name on it.

Say, *What are some questions we can ask about the children in our class? The questions should have yes or no answers.* Some samples follow:

- Have you lost more than two teeth?
- Do you have curly hair?
- Do you like to go to the park?
- Do you have a pet?

Have the children answer a question by placing their name cards in one or the other yarn loop. When all of the name cards have been placed, ask the children what things they have found out by looking at the arrangements.

LOGIC AND ALGEBRA LITERATURE LIST

Ahlberg, Janet, and Allen. *The Baby's Catalogue.* New York: Little, Brown, and Co., 1983.

Baratta-Lorton, Mary. *Mathematics Their Way.* Menlo Park, CA: Addison-Wesley, 1976.

Hoberman, Mary Ann. *A House Is a House for Me.* New York: Viking, Penguin, 1978.

Nozaki, Akihiro, and Mitsumasa Anno. *Anno's Hat Tricks.* New York: Philomel Books, 1985.

Reid, Margarette S. *The Button Box.* New York: Dutton Children's Books, 1990.

Slobodkina, Esphyr. *Caps for Sale.* New York: HarperCollins Children's Books, 1947.

Zolotow, Charlotte. *Mister Rabbit and the Lovely Present.* New York: HarperCollins Children's Books, 1962.

Measurement

MEASUREMENT AS A REAL-WORLD APPLICATION

Measurement is a child's natural introduction to mathematics. Early comparisons such as *I'm taller than you,* or *My cookie is bigger,* lead to questions of *How much taller?* and *How much bigger?* The activities in this section lead children to use and compare numbers as they measure the lengths of various parts of their bodies, the distances their paper airplanes fly, and how far their toy cars roll down ramps of different heights.

In addition to length, other activities in this section give children opportunities to measure volume by measuring ingredients for cooking projects and designing aluminum foil boats to carry the most beans. By tracing each other's bodies, children get to see the area that their bodies take up. These investigations give children wonderful ways to measure distance, area, and volume in enjoyable ways.

What do the experts say?

You cannot tell children how to measure; they should be provided with materials . . . and be allowed to experiment and try to solve measurement problems for themselves. The teacher should play the role of questioner in moving toward the objective desired, in this case, measurement.

Richard W. Copeland
How Children Learn Mathematics

Who Sank the Boat?

LITERATURE CONNECTION

 Read the book *Who Sank the Boat?* by Pamela Allen (Putnam, 1982). Use the story as an informal introduction to a study of buoyancy. Provide the children with aluminum foil or clay. Have them use the foil or clay to make boats of different sizes and shapes. Then have the students fill the boats with beans to see how many beans it takes to sink each one. This is also an enjoyable way to practice counting.

You can extend this activity by having the children experiment with the placement of the beans in their boats. Ask, *Does it matter where you put the beans? What happens if you put all of them in one end of your boat? What if you spread them out all over the bottom?*

Conclude this activity with a discussion. Talk about which boats held the most beans and what kind of design they had. Ask the children how they think people load big ships in real life.

Measurement Contests

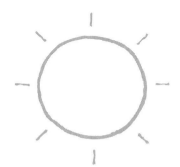

PHYSICAL EDUCATION CONNECTION

Create great excitement over measurement by holding Measurement Contests. There are many events that you can stage; here are some specific suggestions.

■ Javelin Throw
Provide students with drinking straws. Have them toss the straws from a starting point and measure how far they go. Have each contestant make three attempts, recording the distance of each.

■ Shot-put
Students try to throw a cotton ball as far as they can. Each gets three tries and records the distance of each attempt.

■ Standing Broad Jump
From a standing position, with both feet together, a child jumps as far forward as possible. A partner measures the jump, from the heel back to the starting line, and records the distance. Repeat twice.

■ Running Broad Jump
If you have room, the children will enjoy doing a Running Broad Jump. They need a running start, beginning each jump at the starting line. Repeat twice, having partners measure and record the distance.

Ramps and Rollers

SCIENCE CONNECTION

 During this activity, children will get an opportunity to explore the relationship between the height of a ramp and the distance a toy car will roll. It is an excellent introduction to potential and kinetic energy.

Wrap the edges of a large table with cardboard or tape so the cars won't fly off the table. Provide the children with a supply of ramps made of blocks of different sizes and several toy cars or marbles. You may want to have the children tape the blocks to the table so that they don't move.

Have each child place a toy car or marble at the top of a ramp and let it go. Then the child measures the distance from the end of the ramp to where the car is, using a ruler or linking cubes, and records the distance on paper. Have the children repeat their experiments using different ramps.

Let them compare their results by discussing questions such as these:

- Which ramp made the car go furthest? Why do you think this was so?
- How come a car moves even though you don't push it?
- How far do you think a car will roll if you start it halfway down the ramp?
- What was the longest distance a car rolled? The shortest?

Tom Thumb

MULTICULTURAL CONNECTION

The Oryx Multicultural Folktale Series (Phoenix, AZ, Oryx Press, 1993) contains a collection of worldwide *inchling,* or *thumbling,* stories. Read the story *Tom Thumb* to your students.

You might look for some stories that match your students' countries of origin and read those next. Otherwise, start with the Burmese tale *Little Thumb Conquers the Sun,* which is artfully told for young children.

Often in these stories natural or common household items are used for furniture (a nut shell bed), weapons (a needle sword), and such. The children could decide just how big (or small) such items would have to be for a creature just one inch high. Have them collect household implements for inchlings, as many different kinds of beds, tables, chairs, utensils, tools as they can think of — whatever an inchling might need or desire.

Body Sculptures

ART CONNECTION

 Provide each pair of children with two large sheets of butcher paper cut longer and wider than the children's measurements. Have the children take turns tracing each other's bodies on the sheets. Next the children should measure the height of their body tracings using cubes, student-made rulers, or conventional rulers.

Then the children can paint or color their body tracings. There are paints and markers available in a variety of skin tones. When the paint has dried, staple the tracing to another large sheet of paper, leaving an opening for stuffing the body sculpture with newspaper. After stuffing, trim each sculpture around the edge with scissors.

These sculptures make a wonderful classroom display. They are also fun to place in the children's seats on back-to-school night.

Measurement Munchies

COOKING CONNECTION

 To practice measuring with your class, make cookies or some other treat. Display a rebus (for younger children) or a written version of the recipe at the cooking table. Invite the children to take turns measuring the ingredients. You may want to make just half or a quarter of the cookie recipe at a time so that more children get turns to measure.

The following recipe makes one cupcake, which enables each child to have a measuring experience:

Pumpkin Cupcakes

2 tablespoons yellow cake mix
3 teaspoons pumpkin pie filling mix
1 tablespoon beaten egg
4 chocolate chips

Have a child measure each of the first three ingredients into a bowl, mix them, and then pour the mixture in one cup of a cupcake pan. Top with the chocolate chips. Bake at 350 degrees for 20 minutes.

Provide other measuring spoons and cups at the water table so that children can be measuring while others are preparing their cupcakes.

In the Doctor's Office

DRAMATIC PLAY CONNECTION

Set up an area in the classroom to resemble a doctor's office or hospital. Provide equipment such as a floor scale, tape measure, bandages, and stethoscope. Have children take turns playing the roles of doctor, nurse, and patient.

Encourage the doctors and nurses to use the measuring equipment to find out about their patients. Some measurement questions they could keep in mind are:

- How much does your patient weigh?
- How tall is your patient? How long are her legs? Her arms?
- Can you find your patient's heartbeat? Is it fast or slow?
- Have your patient jump up and down for a minute. Is his heart going faster or more slowly now?
- How long are the bandages you need to apply? How much will you cut off?

Seesaw Computer Fun

TECHNOLOGY CONNECTION

The Busy World of Richard Scarry Busytown,
Paramount Interactive
Macintosh, IBM/Compatible

Using this software program children learn about measurement and see delightful characters in action. Show the children how to select the Seesaw playground. They help Lowly Worm move the characters onto a seesaw to see if they'll balance.

Experiment by placing a different character on each end of the seesaw. To move a character onto the seesaw, click it. Those on green circles move onto the right side; those on pink circles move onto the left. To remove a character, click on its circle. The children try to find out which character is heaviest, lightest, and which characters balance the seesaw.

Other mathematical concepts in Busytown are shape recognition, sequencing, problem solving, classification, patterns, counting, and simple addition and subtraction.

Paper Airplane Contest

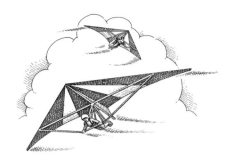

SCIENCE CONNECTION

 Children love to fold and fly paper airplanes. Provide them with a stack of recycled paper and some books from the library about paper airplane folding. Your students and their creations will take off. You can introduce vocabulary such as *lift, nose, wing,* and so on.

After the class has perfected their manufacturing of paper airplanes, announce that you will hold a paper airplane contest. The plane going the farthest will be the winner. Have the children decide where to hold the contest. Provide yardsticks or metersticks to measure the distance of the flights. Have the children record the distance that their airplane flies on each of three trials.

You could also have an award for the plane that remains aloft for the longest period of time. Time the flights with a stop watch or any watch having a timer.

Conclude this activity by discussing what attributes caused a plane to go the farthest and what helped a plane to remain in the air the longest.

A Big Foot

LITERATURE CONNECTION

 Read the book *How Big Is a Foot?* by Rolf Myller (Dell, 1962). It tells the story of a king who wants to have a bed made for his queen as a birthday present. He measures around the queen with his king-sized feet and sends the orders out to have a bed made that is three feet by six feet. The apprentice uses his apprentice-sized feet (which, of course, are much smaller) to pace off the three and six feet. The bed is delivered and is much too small for the queen. The problem is then resolved by making the king's foot size the standard unit of length.

Children love to act out this story as it is read. They see that the bed is going to be too small, and that causes great excitement. Have them suggest solutions to the problem before you read the ending. Ask, *How could this problem have been prevented?*

This is a good book to read before introducing the standard units of measurement, because it helps children realize how necessary standard units are in solving problems in the real world.

MEASUREMENT LITERATURE LIST

Adams, Pam. *Ten Beads Tall.* Sudbury, MA: Playspaces, 1989.

Allen, Pamela. *Who Sank the Boat?* New York: Putnam Publishing Group, 1983.

Briggs, Raymond. *Jim and the Beanstalk.* New York: Putnam, 1989.

Carle, Eric. *Papa, Please Get the Moon for Me.* Saxonville, MA: Picture Book Studio, 1986.

Carroll, Lewis. *Alice's Adventures in Wonderland.* New York: Henry Holt and Co., 1985.

Copeland, Richard W. *How Children Learn Mathematics.* Richard W. Copeland, 1979.

Hoban, Tana. *Big Ones, Little Ones.* New York: Greenwillow Books, 1976.

_____. *Is It Larger? Is it Smaller?* New York: Greenwillow Books, 1985.

Krauss, Ruth. *The Carrot Seed.* New York: Harper and Row, 1945.

Lionni, Leo. *Inch By Inch.* New York: Astor-Honor, 1962.

Myller, Rolf. *How Big is a Foot?* New York: Dell, 1962.

Oryx Multicultural Folktale Series. Phoenix, AZ: Oryx Press, 1993.

Pienkowski, Jan. *Sizes.* New York: Simon and Schuster, 1983.

Shelby, Anne. *We Keep a Store.* New York: Orchard Books, 1990.

Wolkstein, Diane. *8,000 Stones: a Chinese Folktale.* New York: Doubleday, 1972.

Ziefert, Harriet. *Measure Me.* New York: HarperCollins Children's Books, 1991.

Probability and Statistics

WHAT ARE THE CHANCES?

During their time in kindergarten, first, and second grades, children need many experiences with simple games and investigations that involve following rules, making predictions and seeing what happens, and managing the problem of keeping track of scores. Through these experiences, the students will find that with probability there is no absolute answer to specific questions, just an idea of what to expect. They will also begin to make the connection between the intuitive notion of probability and the numerical basis for probability.

In later years, the children will be introduced to probability and statistics, the formal studies of chance events. Until then, give your students plenty of opportunities to gather information, discuss likely and unlikely events, take surveys of their classmates on subjects of their choosing, and interpret the results. This is the best foundation that they can receive.

What do the experts say?

Statistics and probability are important links to other content areas, such as social studies and science. They also can reinforce communication skills as children discuss and write about their activities and their conclusions. Within mathematics, these topics regularly involve the uses of number, measurement, estimation, and problem solving.

National Council of Teachers of Mathematics
Curriculum and Evaluation Standards for School Mathematics

Predicting Endings

LITERATURE CONNECTION

Read the Indian transformation fable *Once a Mouse* by Marcia Brown (Scribners, 1961) and have the children discuss the ending.

Then read or use the flannel board to tell the Grimm tale "The Fisherman and His Wife." Stop after a few transformations and ask the children if they can predict the ending. Write down their predictions. Ask them, *What clues do you have to support your prediction?* Finish reading the story. Discuss the ending in light of the students' predictions. Ask, *Were you surprised or did you accurately predict the ending?*

To point out another author's artistry, with the absence of a predictable folklore pattern, try the same thing with William Steig's *Sylvester and the Magic Pebble* (Simon and Schuster, 1973).

Ask the class if the endings of some stories are harder to predict than others? Do they prefer surprise endings? Why or why not?

On chart paper begin two lists, one of books and stories that have predictable endings, and the other of those that have surprise endings. Continue to add to the lists as the year progresses.

Chance Collages and Probability Paintings

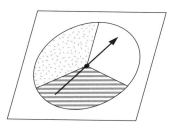

ART CONNECTION

 During these two activities, the children use probability to create artwork. You can have the children work independently or in cooperative groups.

To make Chance Collages give the children different colors of construction paper and glue. Have them make, or provide them with, spinners that have different colors on them. The colors shown on the spinners should correspond to the colors of paper the children will use. Have them use the spinners to determine what color to make each element in their picture. You can put the finished pictures and spinners on display, and the children can try to guess which spinner each artist or group used.

For Probability Paintings have the students use the same spinners to determine what color paint to use for each element in their paintings They must spin each time they want to change the color of paint. Again, the finished paintings and spinners may be displayed, and the children can try to match each spinner to a painting.

Jan-kem-po

MULTICULTURAL CONNECTION

 This Japanese stone-paper-scissors game of Jan-kem-po may be played by any size group. One player is the Changer who stands in front of the others, and another player is the Observer and stands to the side.

The Changer begins by saying each syllable, *Jan,* then *Kem,* pushing his or her arm forward from the elbow each time with fist tightened. On *Po!,* the Changer shows either an open hand (indicating paper), a closed fist (stone), or two fingers (scissors).

Each of the other players must quickly call out the correct response: Scissors cut paper; paper wraps stone; or stone breaks scissors. The Observer names the first to respond, and eventually anyone who wins twice becomes the new Changer.

The children might then play the American version of this game in groups of three, with each opponent showing her or his hand simultaneously. In this case, the winner is the player who shows the one thing (scissors, rock, or paper) that overcomes the other two.

After the children have played these two versions of the game, discuss with them whether they think the games rely entirely on chance, or if practice and strategy could help a player win more often.

An Unlikely Story

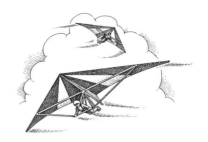

LANGUAGE ARTS CONNECTION

 Discuss with your class what makes an event likely or unlikely to happen. Have the students give examples of likely and unlikely events. Ask them these questions to get started:

Do you think it is likely or unlikely ...
- that a person would wear a bathing suit while sitting on an iceberg?
- that a child would have a pet tiger?
- that it will rain this year?

Tell the children that you are going to have each of them write and illustrate an unlikely story.

First read to them *Cloudy with a Chance of Meatballs* by Judi Barrett (Atheneum, 1978) or another favorite tall tale, to give the students ideas for their stories. Encourage children to use their imagination and rich language in these stories.

When finished, the students can share their stories with the class and put them in a class book, if desired. You could have the class vote on The Most Unlikely Story.

Pugasaing

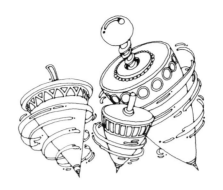

GAMES CONNECTION

 Pugasaing is one of the favorite Native American stick-throwing games, played by two teams of four or five players each. Each team has three sticks, painted white on one side and red on the other. A player shakes the sticks in a basket and throws them to the ground.

Here is the chart from which the players then compute their scores.

Scoring:
3 white sides — 3 points
3 red sides — 2 points
2 reds and 1 white — 1 point
1 red and 2 white — 0 points
The first team to score 20 points is the winner.

Have your students play this game, using popsicle sticks colored red on one side and a basket or can to toss the sticks from.

After they have played the game, ask the children whether they think the game depended mostly upon chance, or if skill and strategy played a part. Questions for the class to consider are:

- How likely is each combination of colors to come up?
- What is the fewest throws a team could make and still win?
- Does the scoring system favor a certain color combination?

Spinner Sports

PHYSICAL EDUCATION CONNECTION

 Here are two games for your class to play that take into account chance and probability.

■ Spinner Relays

This is a game for the whole class. Have children form lines of five to six players each. Give each team a spinner that has different relay techniques written on the different quadrants. For example: Skip backwards; run; gallop; hop; jump.

When Go! is called, the first person in line spins the spinner and proceeds to a certain point, moving as the directions indicate. When that player returns to the line, the second player spins and takes a turn, and so on.

■ Game of the Giants

Before starting the game, make a huge game board, having a path of several colors of construction paper, on the classroom floor. Have the children make spinners showing the colors of the paper in the path.

Four children will be the game pieces. The others will spin the spinners. Take turns having a child spin a spinner for each game piece. The game piece then moves along the path to the next paper of the color spun. The first game piece to reach the end of the path is the winner.

You could play this game outdoors, drawing the path on the playground with colored chalk.

Ancestor Hunt

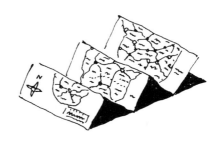

MULTICULTURAL CONNECTION

 Have one child stand in the front of the room. Say that every person had two parents and have two children stand behind the first one. Each of the parents had two parents, so now four children, the grandparents, stand behind the last two. Each grandparent had two parents, so now eight children, the great grandparents, go and stand behind the last four.

Ask the class, *Are there enough of us left to show great, great grandparents? How many more people would we need to show great, great grandparents? Is it likely that anyone knows where all of his or her ancestors came from? Do you know where one or two of yours came from?*

When a child volunteers where some ancestors came from, find these locations on your classroom map. Do this for as many children as seem interested. If the children want, they could pursue the subject by finding books to read that tell about their ancestors' countries of origin.

Invent a Game

GAMES/CREATIVITY CONNECTION

 One creative way for students to learn more about chance and probability is by inventing and playing their own board games.

A quick and easy way to do this is to recycle clean pizza boxes. Children can draw their game boards on the inside bottom of the box. They can write instructions and scoring rules on the inside of the cover. Then they can write the name of their game on the top of the box and add decorations. Any necessary dice, spinners, or game pieces can be easily stored inside the box when game time is over.

It may take children some time to think up and create their games. You can provide blank dice for the children to use; they make spinners. Both of these items will inject the element of chance and probability into the games.

If you have a collection of inexpensive toys like cars, dolls, or boats, the children can use these, and they will also start the children's ideas flowing as the students begin to create their games.

Fruit Salad Surprise

COOKING CONNECTION

Try this probability recipe for salad.

Beforehand you or the children can label some blank dice with pictures of six fruits for a salad, repeating some fruits on the same die if you won't have six fruits to choose from.

Let each child take turns rolling a die, recording the result, and putting one tablespoon of that fruit into a bowl. Determine how many times each child may toss the die, depending on the amount of fruit available.

Each student will record the results and make a personal copy of the recipe. Have pairs of children compare their salads and recipes before they eat them. Have them see if their recipes are the same or different. Ask them if they would be able to tell that the recipes were different by just looking at their salads.

You might want to construct a class chart of the different recipes looking to see how many different versions there are and who (if anyone) rolled the same recipe.

The Mousehole

TECHNOLOGY CONNECTION

The Playroom, Broderbund
Apple II Series, IBM/Compatible, Macintosh

With The Mousehole activity in The Playroom, students will continue to gain experience with probability, dice, game strategies, and counting, Show the students how to click on the mousehole to get into the game. The children will get a choice of three game boards and whether there will be one or two players. Then a game board will appear that has numbers in some of the spaces. If the numbers are in white ovals, they move the players forward, and if the numbers are in black ovals, they bounce them back.

After a player clicks on the dice shaker, the computer rolls three dice. The player determines which of the dice he or she wants to use for this turn. Children quickly learn to read the dice and to count ahead to determine which of the dice will yield the largest move. The children also become adept at figuring out what roll of the dice will help them the most.

PROBABILITY AND STATISTICS LITERATURE LIST

Barrett, Judi. *Cloudy with a Chance of Meatballs.* New York: Atheneum Publishers, 1978.

Brown, Marcia. *Once a Mouse.* New York: Scribners, 1961.

Geringer, Laura. *A Three-Hat Day.* New York: Harper and Row, 1985.

National Council of Teachers of Mathematics. *Curriculum and Evaluation Standards for School Mathematics.* Reston, VA: The Council, 1989.

Nozaki, Akihiro, and Mitsumasa Anno. *Anno's Hat Tricks.* New York: Philomel Books, 1985.

Numeroff, Laura Joffe. *If You Give a Mouse a Cookie.* New York, Harper and Row, 1985.

Steig, William. *Sylvester and the Magic Pebble.* New York: Simon and Schuster, 1973.

CROSS-REFERENCE BY CONNECTION